A red parrot flaps its wings.
A chimp swings.
A pink flamingo stands on one leg.
But can you see the snail?

1

Hens cluck.
Ducks quack.

A black cat sits in the sun.
But can you see the snail?

A squirrel cracks a nut.
A thrush sings in its nest.

A web hangs from a twig.
But can you see the snail?

A boat sails.
A gull pecks at a sandwich.

A crab runs across a rock.
But can you see the snail?

A frog jumps.
A duck swims across the pond.

Seven ducklings swim after her.
But can you see the snail?

Bees buzz.
A man digs.

A robin sits on a twig.
But can you see the snail?

11

Bats flit.
A fox hunts.

12

In the street, the lamps are lit.
But can you see the snail?

A cat licks her kittens.
A dog wags his tail.

A rabbit munches a carrot.
But can you see the snail?

Six pink fish swim along.
A big black fish snaps at them.
An octopus lies in wait.
How many snails can you see?